HAPPY BIRTHDAY, ST. LOUIS!

Written by Carolyn E. Mueller

Illustrated by Ed Koehler

In the year 1764,
    A group of explorers came ashore.
Led by a young Auguste Chouteau,
    They started St. Louis, the place we all know!

Hiss, puff, and chug went the mighty steamboat.
Ships passing through kept our city afloat.
Look to the wheel, is it Mark Twain? Could it be?
Life on the Mississippi was an adventure, you see.

Soon enough, boats went out of style.

Railroads crisscrossed the country, after a while.

Trains carried people and goods at great speeds,

A river-spanning bridge was built by James Eads.

Our city held the World's Fair in 1904,
It delivered a show—a party for sure.
Ice cream cones and hot dogs saw the light of day.
Palaces, parks, and mansions put St. Louie on display.

New York

From New York to Paris, "Lucky Lindy" braved his flight,
Soaring over the Atlantic on a dark and lonely night.
He logged 3,000 miles through the fog and the rain,
Showing that the Spirit of St. Louis was more than just a plane.

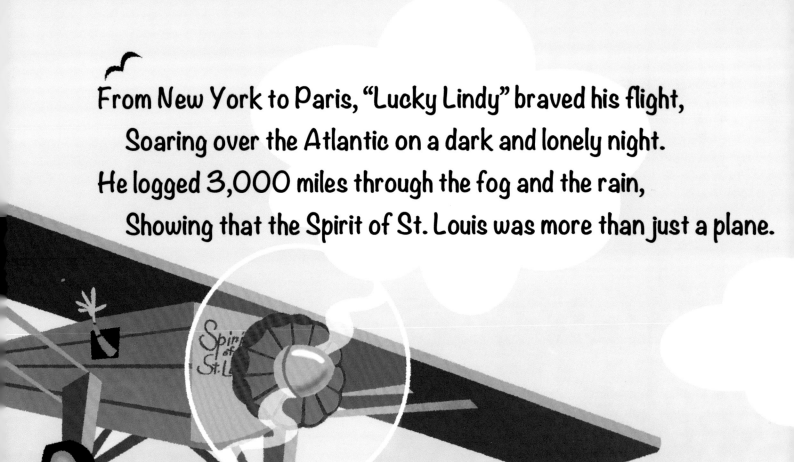

Paris

The World Series was all St. Louis in 1944,
  The Browns played the Cardinals in the midst of a war.
  Two hometown teams looked even in the mix,
  But the Cards took victory behind Musial, number 6!

From Miles Davis's trumpet, to Joplin's piano key,
This city has always been the jazziest place to be!
With a little bit of rock and a whole lot of roll,
Chuck Berry gave the St. Louis Blues a new kind of soul.

Six hundred and thirty feet tall, built of shining steel,
This glorious monument is a very big deal!
The Arch stands over our city, looking its best,
Our upside-down smile is the Gateway to the West.

So let's celebrate our past and our bright future too.
Happy Birthday St. Louis! Happy Birthday to you!
We'll cut the cake and cheer the city we adore,
Happy 250th St. Louis, we wish you many more!

Favorite things and places in St. Louis

List your favorite things and places

_____   _____

_____   _____

_____   _____

_____   _____

_____   _____

_____   _____

To my Mom and Dad, for all of the soccer practices, Cards games,
Imo's dinners and trips to the Zoo. Thanks for raising me as a proud St. Louisan!

—C. E. M.

To Judy, the first and only Dogtown girl I ever met and dated.
And married. You are my Queen of Love and Beauty!

 —E. K.

About the Author

Carolyn E. Mueller is the author of the children's books *Bubbles the Dwarf Zebu: A Story About Finding a Home at the Saint Louis Zoo* and *Lily: A True Story of Courage and the Joplin Tornado*. She is proud to be a native St. Louisan.

About the Illustrator

Ed Koehler is a native St. Louisan who works with publishers nationwide illustrating children's books, magazines, and educational materials. Ed grew up in the Bevo neighborhood and went to Cleveland High School (because he knew you would ask).

Library of Congress Control Number: 2014933461
ISBN: 978-1-935806-78-3

Printed in the United States of America
14 15 16 17 18   1 2 3 4 5